Proverbs

Chapter 16 Verse 3

"Commit your Works to the Lord,

and your thoughts will be established.,"

Maybe even published!

"Don't be intimidated by what you don't know.

That can be your greatest strength and ensure that

you do things differently from everyone else."

~ SARA BLAKELY ~

"Repetition is the Mother of skill."

~ Tony Robbins ~

May YOU read this book repeatedly & learn lots!

www.TheLittleBookofCancer.com

THE LITTLE BOOK OF CANCER

Author Irene Lopez

Editor Jacqueline Diana Lopez

Cover Design & Hand Sketched By: Irene Lopez

Production Managers:

Jacqueline Diana Lopez

Victoria Lauren Lopez

Elizabeth Ashley Lopez

YouTube, Social Media, Public Relations & Special Events please

Contact: Victoria Lauren Lopez

Photography, Photos, Videos & Archives

Elizabeth Ashley Lopez

Cataloging in publication data has been applied for and is available

from the Library of Congress #2020909727

ISBN # 978-1-7348348-0-2

Printed in the United States of America

Publishing Company: The Lopez Cottage Publishing

www.TheLittleBookofCancer.com

Table of contents

Our relationship with God and how we lived & loved with God's purpose in our life as Husband ♥ Wife!

To God **ALWAYS** be the glory!

To God Almighty for gifting me with his Mercy, kindness, wisdom, and love; and for allowing me to be his servant in writing this book for the world to read.

My beloved husband Greg L. Lopez the strongest man I know. All 8 of our beautiful God gifted children.

Special heartwarming thanks to my father Arturo Martinez and my Mother Della Martinez for all those words of inspiration and love; in person as well as on our phone conversations. Also, those special lunches.

Special Love and appreciation to my Father-in-law Charles for always being there for us when we needed him. Charles is now with our Lord. A special blessing for my Mother-in-law Gila Lopez for all her prayers, love and support, and all those special breakfast mornings and afternoon movies with Greg.

"Do all your Giving ♥ Gifting while you are living, because when you are gone the people you wish to "BLESS" may never ever know how much they meant to you." ~ Mrs. Irene Lopez ~

"If you have a <u>purpose</u> in which you can <u>believe</u>, there's no end to the amount of things you can accomplish."
~ MARIAN ANDERSON ~

Introduction

My story from our personal journal and journey of how we lived with cancer. Since the very first moment I heard the doctor tell me, "Your Husband Greg has stage 2 cancer in the esophagus." I could not help but think, where do people go? What do they do? How in the world does anyone prepare themselves for the unknown? I thought to myself. I have two choices:

1. I could give up and lay down and cry.

2. I could ask God for wisdom and begin to fight for my Husband's life! Guess what I chose? I chose to fight and win!

I simply could not even imagine how the human everyday person could even accept a fate so great, so frightening, the "unknown," the "unprepared." I kept telling myself, I must share, I must write this book! So, I got busy and started writing The Little Book of Cancer. It all started with a journal and then I created the binder I had many names for the front cover, and I decided to go with the little book of cancer so that I may share our cancer story with the world.

Hebrews Chapter 13 Verse 16
"But do not forget to do GOOD and SHARE,
for with such sacrifices God is well pleased."

Introduction continued..........

I began to work with compassion and empathy for the next family who goes through what Greg and I went through. I said to myself, I must begin with these three things.

1. BOOK - References and reminders of our personal story to inspire and encourage anyone and everyone to beat cancer.

2. JOURNAL - To write your own personal Journey. Do not forget to celebrate successes!

3. BINDER - To make life easier, organized and take away a big chunk of stress!

May You be Wise & Strong with Great Courage!

Always Remember the POWER of Prayer!

SPECIAL THANKS & APPRECIATION

Our Pastor John Riley & Wife

WACC.net "Bringing Jesus to People & People to Jesus!"

Our Angel Angela Willrich

Special Events Coordinator (562) 833-9093

Joe Villaescusa My Broker **#1 Office in the world 2012**

Century 21 ALLSTARS (562)-863-2121 #1 Office in Calif.

Ross & Shelly Friedman & Family

Restoration-Water & Fire Damage (626) 260-4595

Christopher & Bethany

Restoration (626)-260-4595 & **Alkaline water (909)-767-7009**

Lori & Victor Sanchez & Family

La Vista Sales Food Brokers (909)-618-5545

Rebecca Elayache Romero

Attorney at Law (626) 282-7463 www.here2defend.com

SPECIAL THANKS AND APPRECIATION

Continued..........

Steven Ibarra Attorney at Law

(562) 735-0828 sibarra@ibarralaw.com

Lior Katz Attorney at Law

(310) 444-9444 lior@katzlaw.com www.katzlaw.com

Carlos at Eckles Auto Body Shop and Restoration

(562) 692-0623 Treat you like Family!

Coach Venny & Ana Saucedo

Owner of Farmers Ins. 714-582-1779 Best Customer Service!

New American Funding **Owner Patty Arvielo (800) 890-1057**

Best Rates & Service!

New American Funding **Hamest Manoukian, Sr. LOAN Officer**

(323) 712-3551 Best Service & Results!

Debbie Moreno **Interior Decorator Organizer & Stager**

562-714-8839 ♥ Love where you live!

Our Personal Library on Our Journey to Inspire & Educate Us!

Bible: First book I read every morning with "Our Daily Bread"

odb.org

Lessons By: Gisele Bundchen

The power of asking By: Loralie Klages

    (Chapter 6 Medical - taking control of your health)

Arianna Huffington - The Sleep Revolution chapter 4 The Science

of Sleeping

20 Powerful Steps to a Healthier Life By: Dr. Schulze's

www.herbdoc.com

800-437-2362 Address: 4114 Glencoe Ave., Marina Del Rey, CA

90292

The Cancer Revolution By: Leigh Erin Connealy, MD

    The Be Perfectly Healthy Book By: Leigh Erin Connealy, MD

Sheryl Sandberg – Her book "Lean In"

    Make your Partner a Real Partner, sit at the table, & LEAN IN!

MONEY MASTER THE GAME By: Tony Robbins chapter 6 is my

favorite!

FINANCIALLY FEARLESS By: Alexa Von Tobel, CFP of

www.Learnvest.com **(also on YouTube – TED Talks "One Life-**

Changing Class You Never Took")

Our Personal Library on our Journey to Inspire & Educate Us!

And so many more magazines and articles and websites

Energy Times – Enhancing your vitality through Nutrition, Health & Harmony

Good Health Lifestyles – editorial@goodhealthlifestylesmag.com

Health e Times – Live Life Naturally info@healthetimes.com

Mother Earth Living Natural Home, Healthy Life
www.motherearthliving.com

Better Nourish & Heal – www.betternourish&heal.com

USC Health – www.keckmedicine.org

"We don't need more ventilator's, Doctors or even Nurses.

What we need is more LOVE."

~ ANGELA WILLRICH ~

A Note from the Author, Irene Lopez
"On a Personal Note!"

Our Love Story!

It was the 4th of July 1997, when I asked Greg for a cup of coffee; he then told me he had something to tell me. It was then at that very moment when he told me with such courage and confidence that he had been in love with me for the last few years.

I was in shock! You see, Greg has always been around us, I just never knew he was paying attention. Yes, I was pleasantly surprised. I had been praying to God to choose my Husband, and He did.

It took great bravery on Greg's Part to share with me how he felt. I thank God every day for blessing me with my husband Greg.

We have been sharing fireworks ever since!

A Note from the Author, Irene Lopez

"On a Personal Note!" continued……..

After our very first date, Greg brought me this beautiful frame with an even more beautiful and special poem. He said it reminded him of us.

I Love You♥

I love you, not only for what you are, but for what I am when I am
with you.
I love you, not only for what you have made of yourself but for
what you are making of me.
I love you, for passing over all my foolish and weak traits, that you
can't help but see.
I love you, for drawing out into the light my beauty, that no one else
had looked quite far enough to find.

I Love You♥

A portion of this is from a song by Mary Carolyn Davies called,
"Why I Love You"

Greg's Amazing Medical Team & Our Favorite Places

Dr. Shum – www.theoncologyinstitute.com

Dr. James Buxbaum – Keck Hospital of USC

www.keckmedicine.org

WACC - Whittier Area Community Church - Pastor John Riley

www.WACC.net

Century 21 Allstars - My Real Estate Office www.c21allstars.com

Tim Woodfield Photography, Video 562-587-0941

timwoodfiled@mac.com

Melanie Whitcomb, Naturopath NEO Life Nutritional

562-587-3850 melanie.whitcomb5@gmail.com

Special Princess Club - Greg was Leader for 3 consecutive years.

Much Love!

SHM - Sacred Heart of Mary, My BFF'S from high school ♥ You!

Dr. Leigh Erin Connealy, MD Cancer Center for Healing in Irvine,

CA - 949-581-4673 www.CancerCenterforHealing.com

Tea Rose Garden in Pasadena – 626-578-1144

Elizabeth is the owner www.tearosegarden.com

Friscos is our favorite drive-thru to eat healthy 562-947-3663

www.friscos.com Love the Greek Salad!

"Young People need Models, not Critics."

UCLA Coach John Wooden

"Talent is God Given,

Be Humble.

Fame is Man-Given,

Be Grateful.

Conceit is Self-Given,

Be Careful!"

~ UCLA Coach John Wooden ~

"Everyone is connected. Connect your business to everyone."

~ Mitch Joel ~

Author, Social Media Expert

L.A. Sky Lens Video, Photo & Websites

Thank you for My Website!

www.TheLittleBookofCancer.com

Joseph Cordova 818-850-9536

www.LASkyLens.com

Best Seller in A Weekend

Alicia Dunam alicia@aliciadunams.com

Thank you for helping me finish my book.

Chapter 1

Urgent Care Visit & Emergency Visit at the Hospital

"Yes! Share Your Experiences with the World;

it's worth 8 Billion & Growing!"

~ Irene Lopez ~

Tea Connoisseur, Crochet-knitter, Realtor, Author,

&

Sew much more!

It was Thursday, September 8th, 2011, when my husband started complaining of excruciating pain in his chest and stomach. I thought it was the fried food he was eating off the lunch truck at work. It was not like Greg to stay up all night, he is usually a deep sleeper and hardly ever got sick. We first went to Urgent Care and they had given him a cocktail, no not an alcoholic cocktail, it was a medicated liquid drink to numb his pain. We then went home, and he was able to sleep, as-long-as the medication was working.

The next morning, I took the girls to school and I noticed Greg's expression was like none I had ever seen before. He finally told me, "Okay, take me to ER when you get back from dropping off the girls." My tension grew, I was hit with a flood of emotions. I then quickly dropped off the girls and came home as fast as I could. Greg did not look good at all. I got his medical file, and we were on our way.

Colossians Chapter 3 Verse 12

"And let the <u>peace of God</u> rule in your hearts, to which also you were called in one body; and be thankful."

Having an individual medical file for each of us helps me keep track of appointments, visits to the doctors, dentist, eye doctors, prescriptions, and individual medical records for the current year.

I had Greg's file with me as we walked into the emergency room, Greg was seen immediately. It was then we knew it was serious. Greg and I would not come home that day. So, now our journey begins.

I had no clue as to what would occur in the next 2 hours, let alone the next two days. It turned into an ongoing Journey. And now the journey begins.

"The fastest way to break the cycle of perfectionism & become fearless, is to give up the idea of doing it perfectly - Indeed to embrace uncertainty & imperfection."

~ Arianna Huffington ~

"You don't have to be Great to start,
But you have to start to be GREAT!"
~ Zig Ziglar ~

Chapter 2

First Week of Testing & Analysis, The Unknown

Doctors, statistics & Medical Team said 14 Months;

God Said 6 Years!

"Never Say, Why Me,

Always say, Try Me!"

~ Author Unknown ~

At first Greg was being observed and tested while medicated for the pain. They first administered a scope, where he is first medicated and then a scope is placed down his esophagus to get a better view of his stomach. This is when the doctors discovered what was seen to the doctors as an ulcer that had developed.

Not one doctor had come in to talk to Greg until one evening while I was with our girls, a doctor had come in to speak to Greg and told him bluntly, he had cancer.

You see not every doctor has proper bedside manners. This Doctor who will remain anonymous, did not have any manners at all. Later that evening when I returned, everyone in Greg's family was in our room. I had not known of this unpleasant visit from the Doctor who had told Greg that he had cancer. When everyone left, he told me in private how he felt and what had happened to him.

"Don't let someone else's opinion of you become your reality."

~ Les Brown ~

Greg and I were both tested on our reaction to the news. I could see it in his face, it was written all over of how scared he was. Thank God, Greg and I have a strong faith in God and believe it will be over when God says it is over. I felt such a strong sense of confidence as if our Lord were whispering in my ear; what to share with Greg and directing me in the right path.

"Life is 10% of what happens to us

&

90% of how we react."

"Don't tell God how BIG your problem is!

Tell your problem how BIG your God is!"

~ Joel Osteen ~

"Darling, don't give someone else your feelings; or you lose.

Control your feelings and you WIN!"

~ Monica Friedman ~

Chapter 3

Ambulance Drive to Keck Hospital of USC

&

Doctor James Buxbaum Official Diagnosis

"You have Esophageal Cancer Stage 2"

"Be more concerned with your <u>CHARACTER</u> than your reputation, because your <u>CHARACTER</u> is what you really are, while your reputation is merely what others think you are."

~ UCLA Coach John Wooden ~

One evening Greg and I were in his hospital room a nurse came in and told us that we received approval to be moved to Keck Hospital of USC to have a special scope done by Dr. James Buxbaum. I immediately gathered Greg's personal things and packed them while Greg rested and waited for the ambulance to come for him.

Later that evening two young gentlemen came and helped us with Greg's belongings and a few personal photos and memorabilia that I had brought for Greg to feel at home, at peace and loved. We were on our way to getting him well!

When they closed the ambulance door, I hopped in the front seat of the ambulance as I put my seatbelt on, I said to Greg, "Are you comfortable Babe? How are you feeling? I'm here Greg." He replied, "I'm fine Reenie, I'm ok!" I then turned around in my seat as we drove on the 60 Freeway. We then connected to the 710 and as we transferred over to the 10 freeway, I had no idea what would happen next.

1 Corinthians Chapter 2 Verse 5
"That your Faith should not be in the wisdom of men
but in the power of God."

Side Note:

Months later I would drive that same route on the listing I had in Lincoln Heights. Since that night when I drove in the ambulance with Greg. Today, and every time I would drive over that same Bridge, from the 710 to the 10 freeway, I would feel such an emotional rush and the tears would drip down my cheeks.

You see, that freeway and location have such strong and deep memories of hope, faith and oh! so much love. It happens every time I drive over that one Bridge. These emotions and visions of my past with Greg are real; and because of this journey I lived and experienced with Greg, I am determined, inspired, passionate and blessed to share this with the world.

"Your Mind is an Instrument, don't let it play YOU!"

~ Gisele Bundchen ~

As we got off the freeway, we arrived at Keck Hospital of USC. I later found out what an outstanding school of medicine it was, and their specialty in fighting cancer.

We arrived late on Thursday night and I remember being taken to our room. I got Greg tucked in his bed with his special Rams blanket and started to put up sports memorabilia and photos of our family and children. I wanted him to feel loved; I wanted him to know that he had all our love, prayers, and support.

It was so important for me to remain logical and maintain a positive mindset. If you have a positive mindset; this is half the battle. Your loved ones and people you surround yourself with are so important. My father, Art Martinez always said, "Show me your friends and I'll tell you who you are!"

"You are the average of the 5 people you surround yourself with."

~ Jim Rohn ~

You see, it is very crucial and healing that you are always surrounded by uplifting friends and family. Especially with cancer or any illness, for this matter; you should be in a calm environment with people you trust.

Always remember, whenever your immune system is at risk; you must stay clear of stress and germs and always feed your body with fruits, veggies, and **alkaline water!**

It was so important for me to remain logical and with a positive mindset. If you have a positive mindset, this is half the battle.

"The Power of Positive Thinking"
By: Norman Vincent Peale

"Believe in yourself! Have faith in your abilities! Without a humble but reasonable confidence in your own powers you cannot be successful or happy."

~ Norman Vincent Peale ~

Greg and I spent our first night at Keck Hospital of USC, and we were told before we went to sleep that Dr. James Buxbaum would fit Us in after 10 a.m.   The next morning at 5:30 a.m. we were awakened and told that the doctor had an opening at 6 a.m.. We rushed and prayed while dressing; through it all we kept thanking God for the day.

It seemed like an eternity waiting for the procedure to be over. I was in the waiting room when my sister-in-law Diane came with our daughter Victoria. We were all three waiting, until Dr. James Buxbaum came to us and told us that Greg had stage 2 esophageal cancer.

I took a deep breath and glanced up at my sister-in-law Diane who started to cry; I immediately told her, "Stop crying, I don't want your brother to see you crying!" I looked at my daughter, and smiled, I told them both, "It is only Stage 2, we have a great chance to fight this."

Proverbs 18 Verse 4
"A person's words can be life-giving water; words of true
wisdom are as refreshing as a bubbling brook."

Dr. James Buxbaum was so helpful, after he saw our concern and realized how determined I was to fight; he drew a diagram of what he saw in my husband's esophagus. I still have that drawing in my journal along with so many events, places we visited and professional doctors and people who gave us advice on being well and living a cancer-free life.

As soon as I could, I called our children and let them know of their father's diagnosis. It was our son who picked us up that day and played us such beautiful uplifting songs of faith on the way home from Keck Hospital of USC. It was such a special blessing for us. I love that our son has always surrounded himself and his family with uplifting friends. We are so proud of him and his beautiful wife and now two blessed children.

Greg and I were so filled with love and such generous prayers that poured over our family. We went to bed that night not knowing what was ahead but knowing that we serve an amazing and awesome God.

1st Corinthians Chapter 16 Verses 13 & 14
13. "Watch stand fast in Faith, be Brave, Be Strong.
14. Let all that you do be done with L♥O♥V♥E.

44

Chapter 4

Our Journey to Recover,

Chemo,

Radiation,

CT Scans,

Lots of Prayers ♥ Love!

"Human beings are unbelievably strong and terribly hopeful about what's going to happen next. Though everyone's faith is different, I have seen that people have faith in goodness. And whenever they get to the end of life, that goodness takes over. They believe that when they leave this world, a peace will come."

~ Julie Freischlag, Surgeon ~

Hebrew Chapter 11 Verse 1

"Now Faith is the substance of things hoped for, the evidence of things not seen."

Take out your Journal, day planner, iPad, cell phone, and get that binder I was talking about. It is crucial that you have a calendar of all your appointments.

I created a binder with tabs as followed:
Please Note I will be publishing this binder in 2021.

1. Calendar - Ask your charge nurse for a printout.
2. Diagnosis from Doctors - Ask your Doctors for your letter of Diagnosis.
3. A list of all medications - Ask your Pharmacist to print for you.
4. CD's, Photos, print out of Doctors notes and Analysis of any, and all CT Scans, X-Rays, Ultrasounds. (You may attain these from your records departments).
5. Explanation and definitions of all chemo's and any other treatments. (Know what your loved one is taking and all the side effects).

**"Remember to live according to your VISION;
Never according to your eyes."**

~ Corrie Ten Boom ~

Always do your own research and always ask questions?

Read the book "The Power of Asking" By: Loralie Klages,
Chapter 6 - Medical Taking control of your health.

Always remember to have a meal prepared or know where
you can pick up a healthy breakfast and lunch. Your loved one is
counting on you for support. Touch their hand and massage their
neck; smile at them and tell them; "You are winning this fight!"
Words are so very powerful. Always tell them; "You got this!"
You must look up on YouTube a video by:

Doctor Masaru Emoto; It's called The Water Experiment or
The Rice Experiment.

Doctor Masaru Emoto, talks about the three jars of rice and the
power of our words.

Isaiah Chapter 41 Verse 10
**"Fear not dismayed, for I am your God. I will strengthen you,
yes, I will help you, I will uphold you with my righteous right
hand."**

I personally told my husband "<u>on a daily basis</u>":

"I am so thankful to God that you are here!"

"Greg, you are the strongest man ever!"

"I thank God for you Greg!"

"Greg, I Love You Infinity."

On our wedding day I gifted Greg with a gold cross.   On the back of it, I had engraved the following:

I Thank God 4 U ♥ Reenie"

WORDS ARE POWERFUL!!!!!

Proverbs Chapter 16 Verse 24

"Gracious words are like a honeycomb sweetness to the soul and health to the body."

Words are truly powerful! I must share this story with you. It was a week before Mother's Day, and my Mother, Della, shared a story with me. When she was in school her **teacher** would ask her to stand up and read out loud in front of the class. As my Mother would start to read; her teacher would say, "You'll NEVER set the world on fire." I just want to say to my Mother, "You just did!"

Here's to ALL the Grandmothers, Mothers, Aunts, Godmothers, Sisters and Women, especially **teachers** who smile and speak encouraging uplifting WORDS to our children.

It is so true, every time our Children, Grandchildren, Godchildren, or even a Neighbors child receives an award or accomplishment;

CONGRATULATIONS! **You! started that fire!**

This is the reason why every time I would drop my girls off to school. I would say to them:

♥ Jacqueline ♥ Victoria ♥ Elizabeth ♥

"You are a Mover, a shaker, & HIS story maker.
Go Today and Make History; because one day You
will!" I truly Believe they will, thank you God♥

Appreciate and communicate to your team of experts and your center of support. Yes! get use to the term, "team!" You Are Not Alone! Always remember your pharmacist is very important; respect your pharmacist and introduce yourself and your loved one. Really get to know each other.

A relationship goes a long way if you just share your stories and goals with your medical team. Always be grateful for your medical team. Just a simple gesture of bringing a tray of cookies, scones, muffins, or fresh baked goodies. You can be fancy or simple, it is all appreciated. It can be as simple as a box of herb tea and a $3 mug you saw while shopping at **Ross, Home Goods, Burlington**, or **Marshalls**. You may visit any gift shop where you shop regularly.

Just remember that your consideration and your thoughtfulness is so appreciated. Always take the time and remember every act of kindness is priceless.

"As much as we need a prosperous economy, we also need a prosperity of kindness & decency."

~ Caroline Kennedy ~

Very important while your loved one is in chemo and you are with them. There will be hours that you will be sitting next to your loved one. Always remember time is of essence and very valuable. Use this time to read to your loved one. Here is a list of books I read to my husband:

1. Dream Big - Staring Olivia
2. Very Good Lives – JK Rowling
3. Ten Powerful Phrases for Positive People - Rich Devos
4. Believe and Achieve - A Collection of Inspirational thoughts and images.
5. Joy - written and compiled by M.H. Clark
6. The Compound Effect - Darren Hardy
7. Proverbs – Holy Bible
8. Psalms – Holy Bible

"We do not need magic to transform our World. We carry all the POWER we need inside ourselves already."

~ J.K. Rowling ~

Chapter 5

The Support of Family & Friends

"When Family became Friends

&

Friends became Family."

Proverbs ch27 V9

"A sweet Friendship refreshes the Soul."

With Every Birth, we receive a Beautiful new soul that God has gifted us with. God breathed life into that newborn, let us rejoice and celebrate **EVERY** newborn child!

As we celebrate the Blessings of Marriage with Love and God's Strength; may we never take each other for granted. But most of all cherish every moment of the sacrament of Marriage in love.

With all our challenges and changes in our lives and in our world, we come together in prayer and are united in God's Grace.

As we celebrate the celebration of life, may we believe in our heart, soul, and mind that there is a heaven and God is waiting for us at the gates.

"The road to our Dreams has many detours."

~ Kurt Warner ~

Here are a few quotes and Bible verses that
brought Wisdom, Peace and Joy to my soul.

Proverbs Chapter 3 Verse 6
"In all your ways acknowledge Him,
and He shall direct your paths."

"If you judge people, you have no time to Love them."
~ Mother Theresa ~

"When you hold on to your History;
You do it at the expense of your Destiny!"
~ T.D. Jakes ~

"Don't look back and grieve over the past;
because it is gone. Live in the present and make it so
Beautiful that it will be worth looking back on!"
~ Ida Scott Taylor ~

Proverbs Chapter 11 Verse 30
30. "The fruit of the righteous is a tree of life,
And he who wins souls is wise." AMEN!

One thing for sure is when you go through life's challenges, you will find that family come together. Our friends grew closer as we would share conversations with tea, coffee, a meal, movies, a walk in the neighborhood, or a drive by the sea.

Special thanks to all the friends and neighbors who left meals for us on our front porch. The meals were delicious and prepared with love.

The Friedman's Ross and Shelly would share their favorite Cuban restaurant with us, we love you! Our dear friends Becky and Jose; with another dear couple would invite us to a special fancy Valentine's dinner. We would share great conversations and laughed all night while making beautiful memories every time.

I would also share many special Breakfast & tea times with uplifting conversations surrounded by Beautiful friends. It really did not matter where we were as-long-as we were laughing and enjoying life. This is very important in healing your soul. Special thanks to you, YOU know who you are!

"The important thing is that your teammates have to know you're pulling for them and you really want them to be successful."

~ Kobe Bryant ~

Lots of Sunday lunches with my Sacred Heart of Mary sisters. Laughter and tears (happy tears) were on the menu.

I am incredibly grateful for my dear friend Denise Bernal. Her words of wisdom will forever be engraved in my heart, soul, and mind.

We also shared a very special, "Tea-Time" at my friend Elizabeth's **"Tea Rose Garden"** in Pasadena, California. It was rejuvenating and priceless, with such enriching and spiritual conversations. The ambience was magical.

My cousins and Aunties from my Grandma Evelyn Rosales side of the family gifted me with a warm, heart-felt birthday party. They spoiled my husband Greg by treating him like a royal king. I love you all and I thank you with all my heart.

My Mother-in-law Gila and Sister-in-laws Gina, Charlotte, Diane with my Niece Missy and Nephews, Domonic and Manual, always making my birthday special. It did not matter to me where we were, if we were at breakfast, or just sharing a cup of coffee. As long, as we were together. We shared our true lives together.

"If you can't feed a hundred people, then feed just one."
~ Mother Teresa ~

Very special lunches and theater memories with our Extended Family; the Friedman's Ross and Shelly. Our Beautiful Monica Friedman Loved the theatre, Much love to you All!

"Phantom of the Opera"

Greg and I shall ALWAYS cherish those memories.

The phone calls from our nephew Bobby were such a blessing. Those simple phone calls were priceless.

Lunches on the deck with family and friends. Greg would Google Grandma's recipe of how to make green pozole. One weekend we would invite his sisters, brother, and mother. The next weekend, we would invite all our children and grandchildren.

There is something so sacred, so special and reconnecting when we break bread together and sip tea or coffee with beautiful conversations.

"My goal with our American Made Program is to inspire people of all ages to become "DOER'S," whether it's them learning how to make an easy week-day dinner or starting their own business."

~ Martha Stewart ~

Spending time with family and friends was so important for Greg; it was important for him to share this special time with family. Greg had a chance to reconnect with family and friends and share his journey. Enjoying breakfast and a movie with his Mom, Gila were so special. Greg enjoyed every precious moment.

Greg Loved sharing stories with us all and would light up when we would listen, and many times laugh. My husband was very passionate when telling a story. He had a way of making you feel as if you were actually there with him in the story.

Greg loved the lunches, watching the football games with Ross, his brother Gabe and my brother Marc. The Super Bowl Sundays at his sister Charlotte's home were beautiful memories well spent. Going on the road trips with his BFF Joe Rosales (Rambo). A special road trip to a Ram game in Arizona with sons Mariano, and Godson Steven and so many other cherished moments.

"Sports have an Amazing way of bonding people together from all walks of life, building relationships that would have never happened."

~ Kurt Warner ~

One of the most memorable times Greg had was with our Daughters Jacqueline, Victoria, and Elizabeth while being the leader in a Princess Club (A Daddy & Daughters Club). He truly found his place and his position in life. He loved every Daddy and Daughter moment with all his heart. He whole heartedly cared about the men and their lives.

Special thanks to our daughter and her husband (our son-in-law) for taking Greg's place when he could not make the weekend trip to Lake Arrowhead with the girls.

His weekly visits to the Pico Rivera Golf Course were so important to him. Greg and my father would go golfing often. Sometimes Greg's brother Gabe and my brother Marc would join. My Uncle Frank, my Dads brother and my Uncle Bill, my Dads brother-in-law would also join.

Those very special times on the golf course turned out to be such a great time well spent. It was like therapy and a rejuvenation of life. Greg loved every golf game, and he would always make sure to reserve a golf cart for himself and my father. Although Greg was actually very healthy, his cancer would sometimes drain him and take a toll on his activities.

"Reenie look at your last score card and beat it; always compete with YOUR last score!" ~ Art Martinez (Authors Papa) ~

There was one more special time Greg and I both shared and that was with our baby granddaughter and grandson. It was so special and truly a blessing. Greg would love to be with our grandchildren and spend time with them. He knew his time was short. As he grew weaker, he still insisted on being around the babies. Greg loved sitting on his grandpa couch and holding our grandchildren as they would fall asleep in his arms.

There were so many places Greg wanted to visit but we knew it was not to be. So, we planned mini road trips. We would enjoy trips to Carmel, Big Sur, Monterey Bay, Pebble Beach, the Grand Canyon, Palm Springs, Palm Desert, Hearst Castle and Boston. Sometimes, a drive to Seal Beach for a walk on the Seal Beach Pier while watching the sunset was all he needed.

"I am a great believer in traveling; I believe the more you travel, the more you bring back to your day job."

~ Anna Wintour ~
Editor-in-Chief of Vogue since 1988

~ (Evan Carmichaels Top 10 on YouTube) ~

Greg enjoyed Celebrations and holidays. His favorite holiday was Thanksgiving. I would always cook the turkey and Greg would feel like a king in his castle. On Thanksgiving morning, Greg woke up to the aroma of turkey and all the trimmings. I can picture him now as I was in the kitchen cooking with the girls; Greg would call our friends and family and wish them a Happy Thanksgiving. As he sat in the dining room in his special chair at the head of the table; Greg enjoyed his morning coffee and healthy oatmeal with toast.

One very special Thanksgiving; the very first time I did not have to cook a turkey. We were invited by the Bernal's to join them in Palm Desert to enjoy Thanksgiving Day. It was the most stress-free Thanksgiving we enjoyed as a family ever. The Bernal's have been more than friends they are our extended family. Denise has been a prayer Warrior and a beautiful sister in Christ; to me and our Girls. In life it is crucial to have BFF's! (Best Friend Forever)

"Be who you are and say what you feel, because those who mind don't matter, and those who matter don't mind."

~ Dr. Seuss ~

Always remember the people who take care of you: Dr. Shum was Greg's oncologist and fought to keep Greg healthy. He was a professional and a dear friend to our entire family. We will forever be thankful and grateful to Dr. Shum for all his expertise, knowledge, and determination.

Our Pharmacist Tony was more than just a Pharmacist, he was our true friend, and we adore him. Again, always take the time to bring them gifts and reach out to people who you are grateful for. A teabag or a 4 pack of cupcakes goes a long way.

Even our expert on our cars we drove, Carlos at Eckles Has been extremely important and much appreciated. Carlos is a near and dear friend to our entire family. Our youngest son's fiancé at the time (and now wife) had an accident and Carlos gave them the family rate with the royal treatment.

My husband Greg trusted Carlos and appreciated his Brilliant expertise and connections when it came to our cars. Our cars were so important in getting us to Greg's appointments and sometimes ER visits.

"What I'm trying to do is to MAXIMISE the probability of the future being better."

~ Elon Musk ~

Greg worked at Ace Clearwater in the Paramount location. The owners were extremely generous and supported us with continued health care for 5 years, while Greg was on disability. We are forever grateful to the owners of Ace Clearwater.

We also had our contractor Jose **Manuel** Orendain, who helped me prepare our bedroom when Greg had an eight-hour, operation at Keck Hospital of USC. Manuel had his team come Friday and finish Saturday. When Greg came home on Sunday, he would be able to walk around with his feeding tube. We had carpet in our room and needed to change out the carpet and replace it with hardwood floor.

While Manuel's team was replacing the floors and painting, I had my beautiful interior decorator Debbie Moreno help me organize and Stage our kitchen, living room, dining room, bedroom, and bathroom. She blessed us with the fabric for our bedroom and our precious Monica Friedman sewed the drapes within minutes.

"Life can be Art. We all do so many interesting things. I like to see my Passions out and about – not stashed in a cupboard."

~ Rachael Ashwell ~

Greg had a beautiful life-long friendship relationship with Joe Rosales, AKA Rambo. He and his beautiful wife Maria were so instrumental in being there for us in every aspect of what a true friend is.

Rambo has always shared God's word and prayers with Greg. He is one of the main reasons why Greg was such a God-fearing man. I Thank Rambo for all his love and bible verses he shared with Greg. Most of all I thank Rambo for not giving up on Greg.

Maria and Rambo both prayed for us, shared celebrations with us, and broke bread with us many times. They are Godparents to our daughter Victoria. Rambo was Greg's Brother in Christ and led Greg in prayer many times. Rambo's wife Maria is truly a beautiful soul and my very dearest friend and Comadre.

"Material things are not gift's but apologies for gifts. The only true gift is a portion of thyself."

~ Ralph Waldo Emerson ~

I know without a doubt, God has the master plan. He brings people in our lives for a reason. We have an amazing daughter who shares such an unconditional love with her 2 nieces and nephew. Our Daughter and her husband adopted all three precious children.

♥That my friend is true love♥

Those children will always be loved and blessed because of her beautiful soul. I see so much of her father, Greg in her, she is truly a **Beautiful Blessed Angel**.

This chapter can be a book in itself; there were so many incredible blessings. Greg and I were so thankful for so many important moments in time shared with so many beautiful people.

"Life is not measured by the number of breaths you take but by the moments that take your breath away."

~ Maya Angelou ~

Chapter 6:

The New Menu: Changing Our Eating Habits and Juicing!

"Let food be thy medicine, and Medicine be thy food."

~ Hippocrates ~

"THOU SHOULDST EAT TO LIVE, NOT LIVE TO EAT"

CICERO

"Our most precious moments started each day sharing a cup of coffee and reading the Bible."

"Our Daily Bread."

www.ODB.org

As my husband would receive his chemo, I would take the opportunity and read. I have a list of great magazines that you can find online that had so much truth and knowledge about cancer, your immune system and how it works.

We must always fuel our bodies with the best. I had to consider my husband's esophagus because that was where his cancer was. I also had to be sensitive to his bodily functions. We would try different healthy foods that would build his immune system and give him strength.

We would prepare the fruits and vegetables in a juice, to make it easy to swallow and Digest. There were times he had no appetite; we would juice, and he would sip his drink little by little at his leisure, taking his time.

"It is Health that is real Wealth and not pieces of Gold and Silver."

~ Mahatma Gandhi ~

There was a time when he would have a feeding tube in his stomach. This was the most difficult time of all. We enjoyed our meals together as a family. Greg would love to taste the different meals and smell the aromas throughout the house. Although it broke my heart, God had mercy on us all.

If it helped at all, I would look into Greg's eyes and smile. Sometimes we would not say a word, and just sigh, and lay next to each other. I cherish the moments when we would just smile at each other and look into each other's eyes.

Whenever you capture a moment like that; freeze it. Always know that those precious moments will get you through the tough ones.

Hold on to the laughter and the deep sighs of joy; because the ER visits and the heartbreaks are frequent and last all hours of the night till the next day.

"If it came from a plant, eat it!
If it was made in a plant, don't!"

~ Michael Pollan ~

We would do our best to visit our favorite Caffe and enjoy a lovely cup of coffee or green tea with an amazing healthy meal. Our favorite time was when Greg would be feeling so energized and so excited about a new dish that he found on Google. He would surprise us all with an incredible meal. Greg was so proud of his cooking; and rightly so. We loved his sweet mash potatoes; they were like no other. I still have never tasted anything better than Greg's sweet mash potatoes.

I remember one Christmas he decided to make green pozole. Wow! He surprised us all. I mentioned it in chapter 5. It was a beautiful and memorable time.

It is also very important to **drink alkaline water**. I have a list of books that have helped me to prepare healthy meals.

Plant a garden in your backyard or front yard. You can even start an herb garden on your window ceil and in-hail the beautiful fragrances every day.

"The doctor of the future will no longer treat the human frame with drugs, but rather will cure and prevent disease with nutrition."

~ Thomas Alva Edison ~

Really pay attention when you purchase your groceries. Farmers markets are great! Find out where and when your next Farmers Market is being held.

Remember to always buy organic, also make sure to wash your fruit and vegetables thoroughly. **<u>Neo Life Nutritional</u>** has the perfect vegetable cleaner.

Greg's cancer was in his esophagus, so I paid close attention to the texture of his meals and what was best for him. I wanted Greg to enjoy his soups and salads.

When you are ready to enjoy a meal, make sure you sit at the table with your family. Greg and I always shared our "Sunshine & Showers" with our Girls. Each one of us took turns and shared our "Sunshine and Showers". Sunshine is something amazing that happened that day. Showers are what I call sprinkles because sprinkles are something that did not go well that day. It was a time of sharing, and loving, and supporting each other.

"Family and Friendships are two of the Greatest facilitators of Happiness."

~ John C. Maxwell ~

I remember one beautiful Saturday morning we had a breakfast for our children and grandchildren. We were all outside on our deck, and I had the tables arranged to accommodate us all.

We had prepared a healthy meal of French toast, eggs, turkey bacon and breakfast potatoes. It was a time to come together and share each other's stories and lives.

Greg got a little tired and came into our room to relax on his theatre chair that his dear friend gifted him with. Our oldest daughter went in to spend time with her Dad. It was a special time well spent where they shared a heart-to-heart conversation with love and compassion for each other.

I believe more of us should communicate and talk to our children more often. Especially now in a world of texting, facetime, emails, and social media. It is so engaging to have a person-to-person and face-to-face real talk. I will forever be thankful to God for every moment Greg had with each of our children.

"My life comes down to three moments: The death of my father, meeting my husband, and the birth of my daughter. Everything I did previous to that just doesn't seem to add up to very much.

~ Gwyneth Paltrow ~

Here are my top books to read on food:

1. Dr. Schulze's book 20 Powerful steps to a healthier life. Look up on YouTube.

2. Forks over knives – Gene Stone, T. Colin

3. Beating Cancer - 20 Natural, Spiritual, and Medical Remedies By: Francisco Contreras, MD and Daniel Kennedy, MC from Oasis of Hope Health Group

4. Crazy Sexy Juice - Crazy Sexy Diet - Crazy Sexy Cancer By: Kris Carr

5. Healing Spices – www.Instructables.com Edited and introduced by Nicole Smith

6. Be Perfectly Healthy – Leigh Erin Connealy, M.D. The Cancer Revolution - Leigh Erin Connealy, M.D.

7. The China Quick Study Easy Cookbook – Del Sroufe

8. The Taste for Living World Cookbook – Ginsberg & Milken

"I am safe and secure, I exhale any anxiety and inhale calm. As my world expands so do my heart and mind. I am willing to stay open and accept all miracles and abundance the universe has to offer me."

~ Kris Carr ~

Chapter 7

The Change in Our Everyday Routine, Schedules and Appointments.

The Creation

of

"The Book"

Hebrews Chapter 13 Verses 1&2

"1. Let brotherly Love continue!

2. Do not forget to entertain strangers,

for by so doing some have unwittingly entertained Angels."

Always Remember:

Wake up early!

Especially if you are caring for a loved one with Cancer.

On the next page I will give you a blank page to help you stay consistent.

Remember we all need a schedule.

Our schedule is our map of our time well spent.

USE IT WISELY!

"How can you squander even one more day not taking advantage of the greatest shifts of our generation? How dare you settle for less when the world has made it so easy for you to be remarkable?"

~ Seth Godin ~

Author, & Former Dot.com Business Executive

MORNING

5:00 a.m. "Tony Robbins calls our first hour of the day,

"Hour of Power!"

I would make coffee and read ODB.org and have my quiet-time and meditate.

5:30 a.m. - Eat a Healthy Breakfast.

6:00 a.m. - Bath/Shower

6:30 a.m. - Review schedule for the day, return texts, emails, etc.

7:00 a.m. - Go to work/Prepare for Dr. Apt.

7:30 a.m. -

8:00 a.m. -

8:30 a.m. -

9:00 a.m. -

9:30 a.m. -

AFTERNOON

10:00 a.m. -

10:30 a.m. -

11:00 a.m. -

11:30 a.m. -

12:00 noon - Eat a healthy lunch.

1:00 p.m. -

1:30 p.m. -

2:00 p.m. -

2:30 p.m. –

"It is not the time that counts,

it's what you do with it that matters."

COCO CHANEL

79

EVENING

3:00 p.m. – Start preparing for dinner.

3:30 p.m. -

4:00 p.m. - Enjoy a Healthy Dinner

4:30 p.m. -

5:00 p.m. -

Be ever so wise with your time.

Always remember to have your patient's medical book handy: (I discussed in chapter 1 and chapter 4)

"A Life worth living, is a Life worth recording."

Jim Rohn

Always Journal!

As I learned how to schedule and manage life with our new routines and E.R. visits, I remembered to be hydrated, well-nourished and calm.

Always remember, as a caregiver, YOU must be well. You will not be able to care for your loved one if you are not well yourself. So, on that note, please take care of YOU!

When you eat well and **drink alkaline water**, munch on seeds and healthy snacks, you have an audience that will follow your lead. Lead your family to healthy eating habits and activities.

Plan to have dinner outside. Visit a local park or favorite place. Set up a blanket or chairs and enjoy a sunset. Breathe in the fresh air, listen to the birds, and feel the breeze on your face.

Let's feed our Body ♥ Souls with God's gifts.
Let's share beautiful conversations with words of
Love ♥ Inspiration.
Let's allow God to use us by changing our lives;
So that we can change our world."
Irene Lopez

I would drive my husband and our three youngest Daughters to Seal Beach Pier. Although my husband was on oxygen and in a wheelchair, walking him on the pier was so refreshing and it put a smile on his face every time.

My husband and I would enjoy watching the sunset from that pier. I must confess we did stop at Jill's Bakery on Main Street to enjoy the **BEST!** cinnamon roll we ever had. If you ever stroll down Main Street; you must stop in at Jill's Bakery and taste the **BEST!** Cinnamon rolls ever.

The Girls were just happy to be with us, and to know that their Dad was actually having a beautiful day.

In-spite of the Doctor's appointments, ER visits and tough times, we would all work together for Greg's wellness and comfort.

"I try to incorporate <u>FAITH</u> every day, to not remind myself of past failures, to learn how to <u>FORGIVE</u> and to <u>TRUST</u> the future."

~ Vanessa Williams ~

The girls would play cards, watch movies, play music, sing, and dance with their dad. I would catch up with my work, clean or prepare for Greg's next day.

More than anything I loved to hear them laughing and talking. Especially when Greg would give one of his lectures on life's little lessons. He always did share his wisdom and his famous stories from his childhood.

I had always journaled, and made sure Greg always had his journal. Even though he left us several videos he produced himself. I love to read his journals. I think everyone should Journal. It allows us to reflect on the days of our lives.

It is good to reflect, review, and rejuvenate!

"Don't think it, ink it!"

~ Mark Victor Hansen ~

Chapter 8

In this final chapter I shall discuss the following:

1. Disability - The beginning of the end,
   "The Doctors told us 14 months; God said 6
   years!"

2. Our New Budget - Financial Goals
   "Always have a Budget!" (A Map for your Money
   AKA Money Map)
   [See the page for Monthly Budget]

3. Closing - Always Remember, Our Last Breath on
   Earth; is our First Breath in Heaven.

**"The more you praise and celebrate life, the
more there is in life to celebrate!"**

~ OPRAH Winfrey ~

Tuesday, September 26, 2017

When my husband was told from his Doctor that he needed every moment and every ounce of strength to be well. Greg knew that it was permanent disability and that he would have to do everything in his power to eat, breathe and stay as healthy as possible.

There were visits the Cancer Center for Healing in Irvine, CA regularly to keep up with his vitamin C through his port. There were his weekly golf games to clear his mind and be outdoors with nature and my Dad and his brother Gabe. Sometimes his friends would surprise him and join Greg with his golf game. Thank you, Ross & Shelly Friedman for ALWAYS being there for Greg. You are such a blessing to us all even till this day! We love you dearly!

"Passion is energy feel the POWER that comes from focusing on what excites YOU!"

~ OPRAH Winfrey ~

85

The two most import parts were his healthy enjoyable **meals** and his peaceful **sleep**. While I was making sure Greg had all his treatments, supplements and outdoors with nature. We shared beautiful walks through our neighborhood in his wheelchair.

We both agreed since he had cancer, I would handle the finances. This is when we had to file a BK because our income was not enough to cover our new medical expenses.

When Greg became ill, we started paying attention to organic instead of the regular fruits and vegetables. It was an overnight adjustment.

On the next page I will give you a monthly expense sheet that I think everyone should pay attention too.

"An Investment in knowledge pays the best interest."

~ Benjamin Franklin ~

Monthly Financial Report

Debtors	Original Balance	Monthly Payment
Mortgage/rent		
Investments		
Living Trust		
Water		
Trash		
Gas		
Electricity		
Med. Ins.		
Cell phones		
Entertainment		
Visa		
Master card		
American Ex.		
Auto Ins.		
Health Ins.		
Gross Income		
Net Income		
Grand Total		

"Formal Education will make you a living;

self-education will make you a FORTUNE!"

~ Jim Rohn ~

It was a learning experience going through the B.K. and it opened our eyes and gave us both so much knowledge on money and finances.

Forever **indebted** to our BK attorneys: "No pun intended!"

Steven Ibarra - Ibarralaw.com 562-735-0828

Lior Katz – katzlaw.com – 310-444-9444

Every day was a gift with Greg, especially on his last days. We were so blessed to be surrounded by our children, family, and friends.

It was Tuesday morning, September 26, 2017 when Greg got up that morning a little slower than usual. He kept clapping his hand on the dashboard, pointing to the light on the Prius indicating that I needed an oil change.

John chapter 3 verses 16 & 17

16. For God so loved the world, that he gave his only son, that whoever believes in him should not perish but have ETERNAL LIFE. 17. For God did not send his son into the world to condemn the world, but in order that the world might be saved through him."

Greg was always such an amazing provider and protector of his family and was always looking out for us. So, I got him up and made his breakfast. I made sure he had a full oxygen tank and gently got him in the car. We were off, not knowing what was to come.

I had dropped off the girls earlier and came home for him. He insisted that I take the Prius to Toyota for the oil change and I did. As we were driven back on a courtesy car by the Toyota driver. I noticed he had a shortness of breath and was having trouble breathing.

I called his Hospice Nurse, and she came immediately, and I sat him in his chair in our living room. It was a beautiful Chippendale with a high back, I had sewed him a Rams pillow to support his head when he would fall asleep on his chair. Only this time he would fall asleep for the last time.

"A Story a true story can heal as much as medicine can."

~ Eben Alexander ~

Author of

"Proof of Heaven"

The nurse had given him a small pill to relax him and calm him down. I sat on his footrest and held his hands and prayed to myself. I asked for God's mercy and wisdom, but most of all strength.

As the nurse told me quietly, "He's gone," I gently closed his eyes; I immediately got on my feet and lifted my hands above his head and said:

"May the army of Angels take you my love, go Greg be with our Lord."

As I waved my arms above Greg's head, it was so peaceful. I felt a beautiful connection with the Holy Spirit.

I will always thank God for such a special, peaceful moment with him.

Luke Chapter 1 Verses 78 & 79
"78. Through the tender mercy of our God, with which the dayspring from on high has visited us;

79. To give light to those who sit in darkness and the shadow of death, to guide our feet into the way of peace."

Greg's mother and brother were present; and they also gave Greg such beautiful blessings and goodbyes.

I will forever be grateful to them.

Our children started to come as they bowed before their Dad and each had their moment with their special good-byes.

Our Pastor John Riley from Whittier Area Community Church gathered us together. Pastor Riley would bless us with a beautiful prayer. As we all surrounded Greg in love and prayers.

WACC.net

"When Tomorrow Starts Without Me."
~ By: David M. Romano ~
Last (4) phrases
"So when tomorrow starts without me,
Don't think we're far apart,
For every time you think of me,
I'm right here, in your heart."

91

After we laid my husband on our living room couch; our daughter (our Angel) brought bags of ice to keep his body maintained before the coroners arrived.

Our Daughter Victoria had been on a Business Academy, field trip and was on her way back. I will always remember that moment when she ran in the living room as she saw her Dad's corpse laying on our couch. The room grew silent and everyone who was in the family room came into the living room to see Victoria's reaction.

It broke my heart into a million pieces that only God could repair, and he did. As we all watched Victoria so gently say her good-byes to her father.

Shortly after the coroners came to pick up my husband Greg. Victoria ran after them telling them sternly, "You better take good care of my Dad."

"A Good Father will leave his imprint on his daughter for the rest of her life."

~ Dr. James Dobson ~

On a side Note:

Victoria was born on July 26, 2000 and when she was brought into this world the doctors immediately took her and laid her in the delivery bed for newborns. Although, her bed was next to my bed, Greg never left her sight. Greg softly offered her his big strong hand. Victoria held his finger and looked into her Daddy's eyes. Greg smiled at her and welcomed her with, "Hi Mamas!" She was in awe of her Dad.

I was panicking because I couldn't see her. While they were cleaning me and the after birth; Victoria had a precious moment with her Dad.

I believe every one of Greg's children had a moment with him. I believe with all my heart that he is still watching over <u>ALL</u> his children.

Proverbs Chapter 22 Verse 6
"Train up a child in the way he should go, & when he is old he will not depart from it."

My husband Greg left us with such beautiful gifts. The gift of selflessness and a legacy of unconditional love. He was given the gift of "time well spent." Greg was truly blessed to attend and share two sons and two daughters' weddings. He would enjoy many Graduations, Birthdays and Celebrations of life; until his very own.

Greg had hand-written his own celebration of life while he was alive. I remember reading it and when he had requested:

"Only if there was time after the children shared, only then could Reenie (Irene/me) speak."

You can imagine how I felt. After being his best friend, soul mate and wife. I was confused. It did not sound like my husband, but he wrote it. I shall always honor my husband even till today as difficult as it gets. I shall honor him until we meet again in heaven.

Proverbs Chapter 31 Verse 26
"She opens her mouth with wisdom,
And on her tongue is the law of kindness."

This was one of the reasons why I had a photo slide show with 3 special songs that were created by a very dear friend:

Tim Woodfield 562-587-0941

timwoodfield@mac.com

My goal was to share our journey with the world. It is so very true what they say, "A photo says a million different words."

The Beautiful Songs:

The Glory of Love By: Frank DeVol

Secret Garden By: Bruce Springsteen

Wasn't Expecting That By: Jamie Lawson

I just wanted the world to know what a truly amazing, Blessed and Loving soul Greg was.

"You can change someone's life in three minutes with the right song."

~ Bruce Springsteen ~

Greg's soul truly lives on…

I believe in healing the World; 1 Book at a time!

In as many different languages as possible!

I have shared my Best and I have Faith that
God will do the rest.

Hebrews Chapter 13 Verse 16

**"But do not forget to do good and to share, for with such
sacrifices God is well pleased."**

Be Well my Friends!

Till we ALL meet in Heaven♥

Made in USA - North Chelmsford, MA
1238978_9781734834802
02.24.2021 1416